JEREM
WORRI
ABOUT
WIN

First published 2020 by Nosy Crow Ltd
The Crow's Nest, 14 Baden Place, Crosby Row, London SE1 1YW
www.nosycrow.com

ISBN 978 1 78800 774 0 (HB)
ISBN 978 1 78800 775 7 (PB)



A CIP catalogue record for this book is available from the British Library.

Printed in China
Papers used by Nosy Crow are made from wood grown in sustainable forests.

10 9 8 7 6 5 4 3 2 1 (HB)
10 9 8 7 6 5 4 3 2 1 (PB)

For Albie, who loves the wind.
Love Mummy x
P.B.

For Huey
K.H.

# JEREMY WORRIED ABOUT THE WIND

Pamela Butchart & Kate Hindley

nosy crow

Jeremy was a worrier.
He worried about everything.

He worried about . . .
odd socks,

shoe-eating worms,

too-crunchy crackers,

runaway dinosaurs,

burnt toast

and evil squirrels
(Jeremy was VERY
worried about squirrels).

He also worried about what would happen
if the zipper on his Big Coat got stuck.
It happened once.

So Jeremy never risked using the zipper
and was always EXTRA CAREFUL.

Jeremy worried about what would happen
if he ate a spotty banana.

So he stopped eating bananas
(even though bananas were his favourite).

Jeremy worried about what would happen if his shoelaces came undone. THAT could lead to SERIOUS DANGER.

So Jeremy took the laces out of all of his shoes.

But Jeremy's biggest worry wasn't spotty bananas OR runaway dinosaurs OR EVEN evil squirrels!

It was . . .

. . . the WIND.

Jeremy was VERY worried about the wind.

One day, Jeremy met Maggie.

Jeremy noticed RIGHT AWAY that Maggie's shoelaces were undone.

That's when he knew it was going to be up to him to keep Maggie out of SERIOUS DANGER. Otherwise, who KNOWS what would happen to her?

But Maggie wasn't scared of ANYTHING.
"What's the worst that could happen?" she said.

So Jeremy showed Maggie his list.

Soon, Jeremy and Maggie became best friends.
(Well, somebody had to look after her!)
Maggie was always trying to do SERIOUSLY
DANGEROUS THINGS like skipping or feeding pigeons.

But Jeremy was always there to show Maggie how to
be EXTRA CAREFUL and stay out of SERIOUS DANGER.

He taught her how to walk without falling through the cracks.

And how to eat crackers safely.

And how to avoid creepy, shoe-eating worms.

But Maggie didn't really listen.
"What's the worst that could happen?" she said.

One blustery day, Maggie wanted to play outside. So Jeremy did his WIDE EYES at Maggie and pointed to his Wind Dial.

"But I love the wind!" said Maggie. "It cleans the dust out of my ears and makes my hair grow long. Come on! What's the WORST that could happen?"

"Well," said Jeremy, but before he could finish, Maggie ran outside.

He had to SAVE HER!

But as soon as Jeremy stepped outside,
the wind caught in his Big Coat.

"HELP!" cried Jeremy as a great big gust of wind blew him RIGHT out of his shoes and up into the sky.

RESCUE
THE WINGED NUT

The moment Jeremy arrived home,
he saw Maggie.

"Maggie!"
he shouted . . .

"I landed on top of the HIGHEST mountain and WHIZZED through the snow with SLED DOGS, was SAVED by a NARWHAL, then got captured by PIRATES and flew home in a MAGICAL FLYING MACHINE!

And . . .

. . . it was BRILLIANT!

And I want to do it AGAIN!" cried Jeremy.
"Come on . . ."

“But what about the SERIOUS DANGER?”
said Maggie.

"Well," said Jeremy, "what's the WORST that could happen?"